Snip, Snap, Snout

Snip, Snap, Snout!

A Waldorf Reader for
Extra Lesson Work

Text by Arthur M. Pittis
Illustrations by Ausa M. Peacock

Printed through support from the Norton Foundation

Title: **Snip, Snap, Snout**
Author: Arthur M. Pittis
Illustrator: Ausa M. Peacock
Editor: David Mitchell
Cover layout: Hallie Wootan
Proofreader: Ann Erwin
ISBN # 978-1-888365-64-1
Printed in China
© 2005, 2010   by: AWSNA Publications
                                 65-2 Fern Hill Road
                                 Ghent, NY 12075
                                 518/634-2222
                                 www.whywaldorfworks.org
                                 publications@awsna.org

This Waldorf Reader Series is dedicated to Rosemary Gebert who was my teacher at the Waldorf Institute in 1980–81 and whose work as a teacher of teachers inspired me to undertake this project for the benefit of all class teachers and their students.

The author wishes to thank the Austin Waldorf School, its teachers and students, the Waldorf Educational Foundation, the Norton Foundation, the Association of Waldorf Schools of North America, and especially David Mitchell for the support that made this reader series possible.

Table of Contents

Godric and the Hare

Godric loved plants, and he loved animals. He also loved the poor and planted gardens for them. He wanted the poor to have good food to eat.

One day Godric saw that a little hare had eaten a row of ripe peas.

"How will the poor eat if this little hare eats all the peas?" Godric said to himself. "But this little hare is a child of God too. She needs food too." The next day Godric saw that the little hare had eaten a second row of ripe peas.

"This is bad!" Godric said. "I must stop this hare, or the poor will have no food to eat." That night Godric waited for the little hare. She came back to the garden, and she began to eat a third row of ripe peas.

"Stop!" Godric said. "Those peas are for the poor. They are not for you!"

The hare tried to run, but Godric was faster, and he stopped her. He picked her up and looked at her.

"I see that you like to eat peas, but it is bad to steal. The peas do not belong to you. They belong to the poor.

The hare was very afraid of the big man. What would the man do?

"Now, take this!" Godric said, and he hung a ring of ripe peas around the hare's neck. Then he put her over the garden wall.

As she ran away, Godric said, "Next time you want food, do not steal from the poor. Eat the wild plants. God planted them for you."

The Ant and the Grasshopper

One warm summer day, a lazy grasshopper sat on a blade of grass. He sang a summer song.

As the grasshopper sang his summer song, he saw an ant pass by. The ant had a seed on her back.

"Hey, little Ant," the grasshopper sang. "Why work so hard? The day is warm. Have fun!" The hard-working ant did not stop.

"Foolish grasshopper," she said. "Winter will be here soon."

"What do I care for winter?" the grasshopper sang. "I have grass to eat and songs to sing."

"You will not sing that song when winter is here," said the ant.

"Tra la la!" sang the grasshopper, and he hopped away.

Soon the warm summer days ended. The cold wind blew. And after the cold wind blew, the cold snow fell.

"Help me! Help me!" the lazy grasshopper cried to the wind.

The hard-working ant was warm in her nest and had a lot to eat. She lived to see the warm days of spring.

But the lazy grasshopper froze on his blade of grass.

The Proud Frog

A big, fat frog was bragging to the smaller frogs.

"Look at me," he bragged. "I am the puffiest frog in the world." He puffed himself up and up.

Just then a cow came down to the pond to drink.

"But Your Puffiness," said one of the smaller frogs, "that cow is puffier than you."

"Humff!" said the big, fat frog. And he puffed himself up and up and up. "Now I am puffier than that cow."

"No, Your Puffiness," the smaller frogs said. "She is still puffier than you."

So the big, fat frog puffed himself up and up and up and up.

"Now I am puffier than she!"

"No, Your Puffiness. She is still puffier than you."

"Well!" huffed the big, fat frog, and he puffed himself up and up and up

and up and up until he

burst.

The Wise Master

There was once a wise master who lived in an old temple. The temple was falling down, and the roof did not stop the cold rain. His students feared that they would get sick from the cold rain.

One day the students went to their master and said, "Master, we must fix the roof, or we will get sick from the cold rain. But we have no money."

"Steal something that you can sell for money," said the wise master. "Then you can fix the roof. But steal only when no one is looking. Then no one will know you did the stealing."

The students were now very upset.

"Our master is a wise man," said one student. "But it is bad to steal?"

"Yes," said another student. "He told us that stealing is bad?"

"But we must fix the roof," said a third student, "or we will get sick from the cold rain."

"We must do what our master says," said a fourth student. "It is not good to disobey our master."

So after dark they set out for town.

One student did not go. He was a little boy who had just come to the temple. When the master saw him, he said, "Little one, why did you not go?"

"Master, I cannot steal. Even if nobody saw me, I would see that I did it, and who can hide from his own eyes?"

The master took the boy in his arms and said, "Only you passed the test."

And the boy grew up to be a wise master, and many students sat at his feet.

The Lion and the Mouse

One day some playful mice saw a lion sleeping in the forest. The mice ran up and down his back.

The lion woke and took one of the mice in his paw.

"Please do not kill me," the playful mouse said. "If you free me, I will help you one day."

"How could a little mouse ever help me?" the lion said, but he let her go.

Later that day, the lion was trapped in a net.

Just then, the playful mouse ran up to the net and began to chew it. Soon the lion was free.

"Thank you, my little friend," said the lion.

"Didn't I say I would help you one day?" said the mouse. "After all, one good deed deserves another."

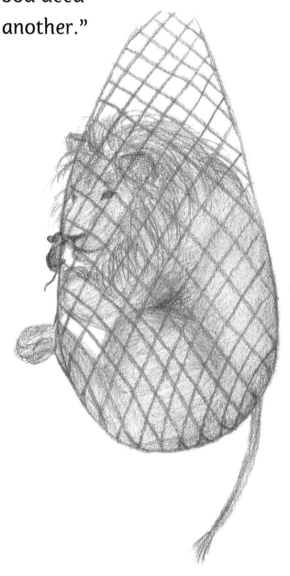

The Falcon and the Rooster

A falcon always came when his
master called. But the
same man's rooster
always ran the other
way when he was
called.

One day the falcon
spoke to the rooster about
his lack of gratitude.

"You chickens lack gratitude," said
the falcon. "You are not noble birds
like falcons. You run from our master
unless you want to eat."

"You don't run from our
master," said the rooster,
"because you have never seen
a roasted falcon. But we have
seen many roasted chickens."

Francis and the Wolf of Gubbio

Chapter One

Brother Francis was a good man. He loved all the things that God had made, and he went from town to town, doing good deeds. One day, he and two holy brothers came to the town of Gubbio.

As Brother Francis and his two holy brothers came up to the town of Gubbio, they saw men on the town wall with spears in their hands.

"Run for your lives!" the men called.

"Why?" Brother Francis asked.

"An evil wolf is hiding in the dark woods!" cried the men. "He has killed ten strong men."

"Only one wolf?" asked Brother Francis. "I will talk with him and tell him to stop his evil ways."

"No, holy brother. The evil wolf will eat you."

"I do not fear this wolf," said Brother Francis. "My life is in the hands of God."

"Then we will send fifty strong men with you," said the men.

"Send just one man to show the way. It is better to trust in God."

❦   ❧

Chapter Two

The next morning, Francis, his two holy brothers, and fifty strong men left the town of Gubbio. Soon they came to the dark woods.

When they heard the wolf, the fifty strong men ran away.

"Run for you life," they called back to Francis. "Not even an army can stop that evil wolf."

But Francis was not afraid. As he walked into the dark woods, the wolf jumped out. The wolf snapped his jaws, and he flashed his eyes. The two holy brothers fell to their knees and cried, "Dear God, save us!"

Francis held up his cross, and the wolf lay down at his feet. Francis could see that this wolf was very old and very sick.

"Brother Wolf," said Francis, patting the wolf's head, "you have done many evil things. The people of Gubbio want to kill you. But I want to give you life. If you promise to stop your evil ways and live in peace, no one will ever hunt you again."

The wolf wagged his tail.

"Now, Brother Wolf," Francis said, "give me your promise."

The wolf lifted its paw and gently placed it in Francis' hand. Then the wolf licked Francis' hand.

"Thank you, Brother Wolf," Francis said. "You may come with me to the town."

"A miracle! Thank God! A miracle! Thank God!" the two holy brothers cried.

But when the fifty strong men (they had felt ashamed of running away and had come back) heard the holy brothers' cries, they said, "Thank God, the wolf is dead!"

ഇ   ര

Chapter Three

Francis led the wolf back into the town of Gubbio. The people did not know what to do. Some hid. Some ran away. And some prayed to God.

"Do not be afraid," Francis called to the people. "Brother Wolf has promised that he will never do another evil thing."

Then Francis said to the wolf, "Brother Wolf, let these good people see your promise."

The wolf lifted his paw, and Francis took it. Then the wolf licked Francis' hand.

"Brother Wolf," Francis said, "If you keep your word, these people will always treat you well."

"A miracle!" the people cried.

"Now, let us sing a song of joy to God," Francis said. And all the people and even the wolf sang a song of joy to God.

After Francis left Gubbio, the people made the wolf a little hut. Twice a day, they gave him fresh water and food, and he never again did another evil thing.

The Crow and the Jug

One day, a crow saw a water jug, so she flew down to get a drink.

She put her beak into the jug, but the water was too low to drink. She tried to push the jug over and spill the water out, but the jug was too big for her to push over.

She was about to give up and fly away when she saw a pile of stones. She picked up the stones, one by one, and dropped them into the jug. The water rose a little bit with each stone, and soon she had her drink.

"Let that be a lesson," she said to herself. "She who gives up never gets what she needs."

The Turtle Who Talked too Much

Two geese lived in a pond. They were friends with a turtle who lived there too. This turtle liked to talk, but he talked too much.

One hot summer the pond dried up.

The geese were going to fly away but said to each other, "What about the turtle? What will he do? Without water, he will die."

So the geese said to the turtle, "We will take you to a new pond. Take this

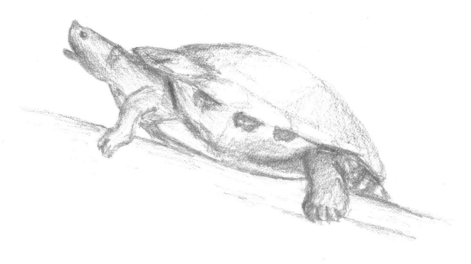

stick in your mouth. But you must not talk when the stick is in your mouth. You must keep your mouth shut."

The turtle took the stick in his mouth, and they lifted him into the sky.

Just then a boy and a girl looked up at the sky and saw the geese and the turtle in the sky.

"Look at the silly turtle in the sky!" cried the girl. "Doesn't he know that turtles can't fly."

The turtle did not like what the girl said, so he opened his mouth and said, "Keep your mouth shut!"

And as soon as he opened his mouth, he fell.

"Poor turtle," said the geese as they flew away. "He never knew when to keep his mouth shut."

The Hole in the Grain Bin

A mouse had her nest under a grain bin. There was a little hole in the bin, and this little hole let grain fall into her nest.

One day she said to herself, "I'll treat the other mice to a feast."

So she chewed the hole bigger.

"Now I can treat the other mice to a feast," she said.

"You should see my nest," she said to the other mice. "I always have a lot to eat. Let me treat you to a feast."

But when they got to her nest, the grain had stopped falling into her nest.

The farmer had seen the hole — now that it was bigger — and stopped it up.

A Basket of Problems

There once was a holy man who lived in a hut on a mountain top. His name was Sadat, and he spent all his days praying to God.

One day some people came to Sadat for help. They all had problems, and all their problems were bad.

"My problem is very bad," said one man. "Let me go first."

"No, your problem is not as bad as my problem," said a woman. "Let me go first!"

"Wait your turn," said another man. "My problem is very, very bad. I must go first."

"No problem is as bad as my problem," said another woman. "That is why I must go first."

So all the people pushed and pushed and pushed.

At last, Sadat came out to see them.

"Stop this pushing and sit down!" he said.

In his hand was a basket. And in the basket were little bits of paper and chalk. He gave a little bit of paper and a little bit of chalk to each man and woman.

"Now," Sadat said, "you must write your problem on the paper and put it in this basket."

The people wrote their problems on the bits of paper and put the bits of paper in the basket.

Sadat held out the basket and said, "Now, pick a bit of paper, but do not read it until all of you have picked."

When all the people had picked, Sadat said, "Now, you may read."

All the people read the problems on the bits of paper.

"What a bad problem!" said some of the people.

"Thank God, this problem isn't my problem!" said others of the people.

"Now," said Sadat, "who wants to trade their problem for the problem that you picked?"

Nobody spoke.

And one by one, the people thanked Sadat and walked away.

The Fox and the Grapes

One day a red fox came upon some big, blue grapes. But the grapes were up in a tree.

"Those big blue grapes look good," the red fox said to himself. "I want them."

So he tried to get them. He tried, and he tried, and he tried. He tried again and again, but they were too far away.

At last, the red fox said to himself, "Who wants those old grapes anyway? I bet they are sour."

Bell the Cat

There was once a cat who hunted mice day and night. One night the mice held a meeting.

"What can we do about the cat?" said one mouse. "She will eat us all."

"Yes, yes!" all the mice said.

"We need to stop her!"

"Yes, yes, yes!" all the mice said.

One mouse jumped up and said, "Death to the cat! Long live the mice!"

"To war!" another mouse said.

"To war! To war! To war!" all the mice said again and again and again.

"Fools!" said a mother mouse. "You talk big, but the cat is bigger. She will eat you all. We need to find a better way than war."

"Let us put a bell on the cat. Then we will hear her," said a little mouse.

"Yes! Yes! Yes! A bell, a bell, a bell!" all the mice said again and again.

The mice were now very happy. They danced about, jumping with joy.

The little mouse even had a little bell. It was a fine bell with a nice ring.

"There is just one problem," said the oldest mouse.

All the mice looked at him and asked, "What problem? This is a fine bell, and it has a nice ring!"

"Tell me," the old mouse asked, "who will bell the cat?"

Feeding His Clothes

One day a Sultan held a great feast and invited all the fine people in his land. He also said that the poor people could come to the feast as well.

That very day, the holy man Mulla Nasrundin was walking by the Sultan's palace. When the holy man smelled the fine food, his belly began to growl.

"Do not growl, my good belly," the holy man said. "I will get you some of that fine food." So he went up to the palace and asked to be let into the feast.

"Look at this beggar in rags," said one of guards to the other guard. "Let us drive him away."

"But the Sultan says we must let people like him in," said the other guard. "Let us put him at the very back of the hall. That way none of the fine people will have to see him."

The guards put Mulla Nasrundin at the very back of the hall. But they put him so far back that the plates of food were empty when they got to him. Mulla Nasrundin's belly did not like that, so it growled and growled and growled.

At last, Mulla Nasrundin said to his belly, "My good belly, I think our rich friend can help us."

At their rich friend's house, Mulla Nasrundin asked, "Will you lend me one of your fine robes?"

"It is yours," the rich friend said. "But first eat something with me."

After eating his belly full, Mulla Nasrundin put on the fine robe and went back to the feast. The guards now put him in the finest seat of all.

Plate after plate of fine food was given to him. But the holy man did not eat one bite. Instead, he rubbed the fine food into his fine robe.

The fine people who sat near him had never seen such bad manners. At last, one of the fine people said, "Sir, where are your manners?"

"A thousand pardons," Mulla Nasrundin said. "When I first came to this feast, I was dressed in rags, and I got nothing to eat. But now that I am dressed in this fine robe, I have more food than I could ever eat. Isn't it only fair that this robe, which brings me this good fortune, should eat first?"

The Wolf and the Watchdog

A wolf and a dog met one night. The wolf was hungry and felt that he would starve if he did not find food. The dog, on the other hand, was fat and well-fed.

"How do you get so much to eat?" the wolf asked. "Are you really such a better hunter?"

"No," said the dog. "If you had work like mine, you would not be hungry. You could eat all day."

"What is your work?"

"I'm a watchdog. All I do is sleep at my master's door and bark."

"I can do that kind of work!" said the wolf. "Let me go with you. I can begin work right away."

As they walked, the wolf looked at the dog's neck.

"What is that on your neck?" the wolf asked.

"Oh, just my collar."

"What is a collar?"

"It is where my master hooks my chain."

"Your chain!" said the wolf. "Does that mean you are not free?"

"Well, it's not too bad. My master only chains me at day, but he always sets me free at night. It's a small price to pay for all you can eat."

"No, thank you," said the wolf, turning to go. "I would rather be free and starve than a fat slave on a chain."

The Dog and the Porcupine

Chapter One

A long time ago, the dog and the porcupine were friends. The dog was easy-going and liked to help everybody.

One day the porcupine said to the dog, "I live out in the bush. It's not very nice out in the bush, so be my friend and let me live with you."

So the easy-going dog agreed.

The dog gave the porcupine food and a bed. One day the dog gave the porcupine some green sticks.

"Do you know what these sticks are?" asked the dog.

"How would I know what those sticks are?" said the porcupine. "I have lived out in the bush all my life."

"It is sugar cane. It is very sweet."

So the porcupine ate the sugar cane and liked it a lot.

"How can I get more of this sugar cane?" the porcupine asked.

"Go to my field and take what you need, but do not eat the roots. If you eat the roots, no more sugar cane will grow."

But the porcupine did not care what the dog said. He dug up the sugar cane, roots and all, until nothing was left.

When the dog saw what the porcupine had done, he spoke to him.

"You said you were my friend, but you went into my field and dug up the sugar cane, roots and all, until nothing is left."

"Your field?" said the porcupine. "Who said that field is yours?"

The easy-going dog did not know what to say, so he said nothing.

ഌ   ര

Chapter Two

The next morning the porcupine went to another field. He dug up the sugar cane, roots and all, until nothing was left.

Day after day, he did the same thing. Soon nothing was left, so he went into the humans' field. He dug up their sugar cane, roots and all, until nothing was left.

The humans blamed the animals and began to chase them with spears.

"Why are the humans so mad?" the animals asked. "What have we done?"

"The dog is to blame," said the porcupine. "He dug up the humans' sugar cane, roots and all, until nothing was left."

"Foolish dog!" the animals cried.

So they went to the dog's house.

"Dog! Come out here right now."

The easy-going dog came out and asked, "Why are you so mad?"

"You're a bad dog. You dug up the humans' sugar cane, roots and all, until nothing was left. Now the humans blame us and chase us with spears."

"No!" said the dog. "Don't blame me. It was the porcupine."

"Oh!" cried the porcupine. "What a liar! Why do you want to blame me? You know you dug up the sugar cane, roots and all, until nothing was left."

"This isn't fair," said the dog.

"Let us go to the judge in the morning," said the porcupine. "The judge will set things right."

And the easy-going dog agreed.

Chapter Three

Long before morning, the porcupine woke the dog.

"Wake up, lazy bones," said the porcupine. "Do you want to be late for the judge?"

"But it's still black night," said the dog. "Let's wait until morning."

"No," said the porcupine. "We must go now."

So the easy-going dog agreed.

Black night was everywhere, and it was very wet and cold. The dog began to shiver. After a while, the porcupine left the path and went into the tall grass.

"Let's stay on the path," said the dog. "The grass is wet and cold."

"Stop crying, or we'll be late," said the porcupine. "That would look bad with the judge."

So the easy-going dog agreed.

They walked for a long time. The dog became very wet, and his teeth began to rattle from the cold.

By the time they came to the judge, all the animals were waiting. They had been there a long time.

"Where have you been?" they asked. "You kept us waiting."

"The dog is to blame," said the porcupine. "He ran off into the tall grass, and I had to find him."

The judge called the dog to him.

"Stand here before me," the judge said. "Did you dig up the sugar cane, roots and all, until nothing was left?"

The poor dog was so wet and cold that all he could do was shiver. He shivered so much that his teeth rattled. All he could say was, "Chh, chh, chh, chh, chh!"

"Look at him," said the porcupine. "See how he shivers and rattles his teeth in fear before the judge. He acts like he's guilty."

"Yes," all the animals agreed. "He acts like he's guilty."

"Well, dog," asked the judge, "is that all you have to say for yourself?"

But the dog only shivered and rattled his teeth and said, "Chh, chh, chh, chh, chh!"

"Then I find you guilty," said the judge to the dog. "You cannot be trusted. You need to be chained."

So that is why the dog spends his days chained. Oh, yes! It is also why he barks at all the other animal when they pass by.

The Suspicious Disciple

One day a boy saw Master Rumi with a tray of fine food.

"Why does Master Rumi have a tray of fine food?" the boy asked himself. "He told us that fine food is for rich men, and we need to eat simple food."

The boy was very upset.

"Is Master Rumi the kind of man who says one thing but does another?"

So the boy followed Master Rumi to see if he ate the fine food. He followed him across a field and into an old house.

There sat Master Rumi on the floor. Beside him lay a mother dog and her pups. Master Rumi was feeding her the fine food.

Just then Master Rumi saw the boy and looked up him. The boy began to speak, but Master Rumi put a finger to his lips.

"You know your heart is awake," he said, "when you can hear soft cries for help from miles away."

At the Lion's Cave

Once there was a lion who was too old to hunt. He did not want to starve, so he lay in his cave as if he were dying.

When the other animals heard that the lion was dying, they came to see him.

One by one, the animals went into the cave, and the lion ate them. So now he had more to eat than before.

Only the fox stayed outside.

"How are you, my king?" the fox asked from outside the cave.

"Not well, not well," said the lion. "Come in, my friend, so I can see you one last time."

"Excuse me, my king, but I would rather stay out here. I can see tracks going into your cave, but I can not see tracks coming out."

Why the Dog and the Cat Are Enemies

There once was a man and his wife. They had a lucky gold ring. But sad to say, they did not know that the ring was lucky, and one day they sold it. As soon as the ring was sold, they became poor, and the man who now had the lucky, gold ring became rich.

Lucky for them, the man and woman had a dog and cat. The dog knew the secret of the ring, and one day the dog said to the cat, "We must get the lucky ring back."

"But how?" asked the cat. "The rich man has the ring locked in a box."

"Get a mouse," said the dog, "and tell the mouse that she must chew into the box and get us the ring."

So the cat got a mouse, and they went to the rich man's house.

"Don't try to trick me," the cat said
to the mouse. "If you do not get me the
ring, I will eat you."

So the mouse chewed into the box and
gave the ring to the cat.

Now, the cat could go faster than the
dog. She could jump over houses and
even trees. In this way, the cat was
home first, and she gave the ring to the
man and the woman.

"Good friend," the woman said to the
cat, "from now on you will sleep near
the fire."

But when the dog got home, the
woman said to him, "So where have you
been? Why didn't you bring us the lucky
ring like the cat? Out you go! Sleep in
the yard for the rest of your days."

So, the cat slept by the warm fire, and the dog slept in the cold yard. The next time the dog saw the cat he chased her, but she was faster, and still is faster to this day.

Everything the Lord Does Is for the Best

Rabbi Akiva was a wise teacher. Each year, he went from town to town to beg for his students. These students spent all day long studying Torah — the Word of God. One year Rabbi Akiva took his students with him. These boys had never been as far from home as a mouse wanders from her nest.

They took a donkey to carry the Torah, a candle to study it by, and a rooster to wake them at dawn.

When they came to the first town, it was dark. They called to the gatekeeper to let them in.

"Open the gate," cried the students.

"Go away!" cried the gatekeeper.

"But where will we sleep?" cried the students.

"In the field," cried the gatekeeper.

"Come back when it's day."

"Don't worry," Rabbi Akiva told his students. "Everything the Lord does is for the best. Let us sleep in that field. There will be grass for our donkey. We have our candle. And our rooster will wake us at dawn."

They found a place to sleep and lit their candle. But as soon as they began to study Torah, the wind blew out their candle.

"Good master," said the students, "we can not study in the dark."

"Do not fear," said their teacher. "Everything the Lord does is for the best."

A little later, the roar of a lion woke them. It was eating their donkey.

"Let us run!" cried the students.

"Silence!" said their teacher. "Do not fear. Everything the Lord does is for the best."

No sooner had they fallen asleep than they heard the cry of a wildcat. It was eating their rooster.

"Let us run back to that town!" cried the students.

"Silence!" said their teacher. "Do not fear. Everything the Lord does is for the best."

At last, the students fell asleep, and Rabbi Akiva sat watch until day.

"Wake up, my friends," said their teacher. "God has given us a new day."

As they looked at the new day, a man ran towards them. It was the gatekeeper.

"Why are you running?" the students asked.

"Last night robbers broke into the town. They made everybody slaves and took them away. Only I got away."

"Now do you see?" said Rabbi Akiva to his students. "If we had been in the town, the robbers would have taken us away as slaves too. If the donkey and rooster had not been killed, the robbers would have heard them and found us and taken us away as slaves. And if the candle had not gone out, the robbers would have seen its light and found us and taken us away as slaves. So always remember, my friends: Everything the Lord does is for the best."

The Silly Donkey

There once was a king who loved little lap dogs. He loved them more than anything else.

He gave the dogs cute little names, and he let them lick his face. He let them run about his palace, and he let them eat from his own plate. He even let the little dogs sleep on his lap when he sat on his throne.

This king also had a donkey. He did not treat the donkey like he treated the little lap dogs. The donkey had to live in a stall, and he never let the donkey eat from his plate or lick his face or sleep on his lap.

One day a hunting dog told the donkey about the little lap dogs.

The donkey said to himself, "How can a king love little dogs more than a big donkey like me? Maybe if I did something cute, he would let me sleep on his lap. But what can I do? . . . I know; I'll sing and dance for the king!"

That night, the donkey danced into the palace, braying and kicking. All the people laughed and laughed and laughed at the silly donkey. But when the silly donkey tried to jump onto the king's lap, the king jumped up and called for his men.

"This donkey is mad," called the king. "Take him away and lock him in his stall. I never want to see him again."

The Miller Who Tried to Please Everybody

There once was a miller who tried to please everybody. One day he said to his boy, "Well, how about going to market?"

His boy liked going to market, so they put some sacks on their donkey's back and set off for market.

After a while, they passed some women sitting by the road. One of the women looked up and said, "Well, how about that! If that man was a good father, he'd let his poor boy ride."

The miller was upset by the woman's words and said, "Well, how about that! Let us please that woman."

So he put his boy on the donkey's back.

After a while, they passed some old men sitting by the road. One of the old men looked up and said, "Well, how about that! If that boy was a good boy, he'd let his poor father ride."

The miller was upset by the old man's words and said, "Well, how about that! Let us please that man too."

So he climbed on the donkey's back.

After a while, they passed some girls. One of the girls looked up and said, "Well, how about that! What a poor donkey! If they were good people they'd let the poor donkey ride."

The miller and his boy were upset by the girl's words, and they both said, "Well, how about that! Let us please that girl too."

So the miller and his boy got off the donkey and stood in the road, but they did not know what to do.

"I know. Let's please everybody!" said the boy. "Let's get a pole and tie the donkey to it. Then he can ride! That will please everybody!"

"Well, how about that!" said the miller. He was very pleased with his boy.

So they tied the donkey to a pole.

After a while, they came to a river. Across the river was the market, and the market was full of people.

"Well, how about that!" somebody said. "Look at those two fools giving a donkey a ride."

Everybody began to laugh and shout and point at the miller and his boy.

Now, the donkey, who was upset at being upside down, became more upset at the laughing and shouting and pointing. He twisted, and he brayed. He brayed, and he twisted. And at last, he broke free and kicked the miller and his boy into the river.

"Well, how about that!" said the miller to his boy. "Who's pleased with that?"

The Legend of Saint Odilia

Chapter One

Lord Aldaric was a proud and powerful man. Few ever dared to disobey him, and those who did paid dearly.

The one thing that Lord Aldaric wanted most was a son. He wanted a powerful son to fight at his side. And he wanted his powerful son to rule in his place after he was gone.

When the time came for his wife to give birth, Aldaric said, "It will be a man child, and he will be powerful like me."

But the baby was a girl.

"She is weak," Aldaric said, "weak and soft, but she will do. Some day she will marry a powerful man and give me a powerful grandson."

That night the nurse held a candle near the baby's face. The little girl never blinked. The nurse moved the candle to the side, but the baby's eyes did not move. The girl was blind!

When Aldaric heard the baby was blind, he fell into a rage.

"Take it away!" he raged. "Take it to the forest and leave it to die."

The nurse did not dare to disobey. She took the child into the forest and left it to die. But when she heard the baby cry, her heart became soft.

"I cannot let this blind child die. It would be a sin. Let Lord Aldaric think the child is dead. I will hide with the forest people and say the child is mine."

℘   ℭ

Chapter Two

Years passed, and the baby grew into a strong girl. The nurse called her My Little Flower.

But when she grew up, the forest people became afraid of her and talked among themselves.

"I say she is Lord Aldaric's child."

"If he knows she's here, he'll hunt her down and destroy us all."

So the forest people drove the little blind girl and her nurse away.

They wandered for many days. At last they came to a convent. There the nuns gave them a home. One day the holy mother who was abbess of the convent called the nurse to her.

"Why do you call the little blind girl My Little Flower? Has she no name?"

"No, holy mother," the nurse answered. "She has no name."

"How can this be?"

"She is the daughter of a powerful lord," the nurse said.

"What is his name?"

The nurse was afraid to speak.

"I order you to tell me the powerful lord's name," said the abbess.

"Lord Aldaric, holy mother."

Now the holy mother was afraid.

"Are you sure Lord Aldaric is the blind girl's father?" she asked.

"Yes. I saw her born with my own eyes. Now Lord Aldaric will hunt her down when he finds out that she's alive. Please, holy mother, hide My Little Flower from his rage."

"You have my word."

જી &ଃ

Chapter Three

When My Little Flower was twelve years old, a good Bishop had a dream. An angel told him to find a blind girl who had no name.

The angel said, "You must baptize her and give her the name of Odilia. God has picked her to do great deeds."

The bishop looked for the blind girl for many weeks. At last, he came to the convent where My Little Flower lived.

"Who is this child?" the bishop asked the abbess.

"They call her My Little Flower."

"Has she no other name?"

The abbess was silent.

"Who are her parents?" the bishop asked.

"She came to us long ago," the abbess said.

"Tell me all you know."

The abbess was silent.

"I order you to tell me all you know."

"She is the daughter of a powerful lord. I cannot say his name."

"I order you to tell his name."

"Lord Aldaric."

Now, the bishop saw why she was afraid.

"Ah, he is a powerful man, but the will of God is more powerful. God must be obeyed."

As the girl was baptized and given the name Odilia, drops of holy water fell into her eyes.

"I can see!" Odilia cried. "Thanks be to God!"

And all around her shone the beauty of the world.

"A miracle," the bishop cried. "A miracle!"

One day, the bishop said to himself, "Her parents must know that she is alive." So he wrote to Lord Aldaric.

"Your daughter lives," he wrote. "Her name is Odilia, and she is beautiful and strong. Even a king would be proud to have such a child."

When Aldaric read the letter he tore it up and threw it down.

ℰↄ   ℭⱤ

Chapter Four

One day Odilia asked the bishop, "Who are my parents?"

"Your mother is a good woman, with eyes like yours. Your father . . . is a powerful man . . . and . . . ."

"Full of rage?"

"Who told you that?"

"I heard it when I was a little girl. When you are blind you hear many things. Is it true?"

"Yes, my child, it is true."

"I heard I have a brother. Is his name Hugh?"

"Yes, he is a good boy. He is kind and brave."

"Then he will help me heal my father's rage."

"My dear child," the bishop said, "he is just a boy."

"Then I will help him be a man."

So Odilia wrote to her brother. Since he did not know that he had a sister, he went to his mother.

"A letter has come to me. It is from a girl who says she is my sister."

"So she lives!" the mother cried. "What is her name?"

"Odilia."

"Do not let your father know. He will be full of rage."

Hugh wrote back and asked Odilia to come home. The good bishop was against it, but Odilia said, "Nothing can stop me."

₲   ℛ

Chapter Five

As Odilia and the bishop neared Lord Aldaric's stronghold, two children stopped them in the road.

"Help us," they cried. "Our mother is sick."

"Here is gold," the bishop said. "Buy some food and find a nurse."

"Holy father, let us stop and pray for this woman," said Odilia.

The sick woman lay on a heap of rags. Odilia took the woman's hand and prayed.

"My pain is gone!" the woman cried.

"A miracle!" the children cried.

"Yes, a miracle," the bishop said.

From his stronghold, Lord Aldaric watched the bishop and the girl ride towards them.

"What do they want?" Aldaric said to Hugh. "Who is that girl at the bishop's side?"

"Her name is Odilia," the boy said.

"Odilia!" Aldaric raged. "How dare you say that name?"

And he hit Hugh so hard that the boy fell from his horse. As Hugh fell he hit his head, and Aldaric turned to go.

Odilia jumped from her horse and took her brother in her arms, but he was dead. She burst into tears, and her tears fell onto the boy.

Then Odilia said, "He lives!"

"A miracle!" the bishop cried.

Aldaric stopped and turned. He rode back to the girl and the boy in her arms. He looked long into the girl's powerful eyes. She did not turn away.

"Pick him up and bring him inside," Aldaric said. "And you, daughter, follow me."

Chapter Six

One day, Aldaric called Odilia to him.

"You will marry a powerful lord and give me powerful grandsons."

"No, Father. I will not marry. My life belongs to God."

"You dare to disobey me?"

"I dare to obey God."

He moved to hit her, but she stood firm.

"Get out of my sight," he raged.

So Odilia fled.

The next day, Aldaric called his men and said, "Bring my daughter here."

They dared not say a word.

"Bring her here, I say."

At last, one man spoke. "My Lord, she's fled.

"Then bring my dogs. We have hunting to do."

Aldaric and his men hunted Odilia for many days. At last, they hunted her down and trapped her against a high rock wall.

"Mother of God," she cried, "save me."

Suddenly, the rock wall split open. Aldaric's horse reared up and fell to the side. Then just as suddenly, the rock wall shut around her.

Then deep in her heart, she heard her father cry out in pain. She called to the rock to open, and once again it split open.

There on the ground lay Aldaric. His horse had fallen on him. He was in pain. She pushed her way past his men and dogs.

"Father," she said gently, "I've come to heal you."

And when her tears fell on him, he was made well again.

Lord Aldaric became a man of peace, and he gave Odilia his great stronghold. There she built a hospital where, to this day, the sick and blind come to be healed.

Origins of Stories

The Legends

The Fables

Author and Illustrator

Author:

Arthur M. Pittis has been a class and high school humanities and theater teacher in Waldorf schools since 1981, first at the Waldorf School of Baltimore and now at the Austin Waldorf School. He is the author of Pedagogical Theatre and is a member of the Leadership Council of AWSNA, and currently serves as the AWSNA Accreditation Coordinator. He is the father of two adult daughters who received Waldorf educations.

Illustrator:

Ausa M. Peacock attended the Austin Waldorf School from kindergarten through twelfth grade. She is a graduate of Queens University in Kingston, Ontario where she studied fine arts. In illustrating this series, she called upon her experience as a student in the Waldorf school in creating her warm and evocative drawings.

For the Teacher

The *Waldorf Reader Series* is designed to serve as an instructional tool for the teaching of reading from printed texts. *Fee Fi Fo Fum* is the first book in the series, and *As My Heart Awakes* and *When I Hear My Hear Singing* follow. *Snip, Snap, Snout* is designed for Extra Lesson work and consists of selected stories from *As My Heart* and *When I Hear*, thereby allowing the whole class to work with the same stories despite being divided into different instructional groups. *Sun So Hot I Froze to Death* is the final book and introduces the young reader to non-standard English and a variety of narrative styles and voices. It is not recapitulative and serves as a bridge to the corpus of children's literature that becomes accessible once a class has developed its reading skills.

The stories compliment the Waldorf language arts curriculum and are intended for recapitulative use in reading skills classes some time removed from when the story genre was introduced in main lesson. The series is also designed to be worked with sequentially in that the vocabulary and sentence structures used develop incrementally in sophistication from story to story and book to book. While it is not absolutely necessary for the teacher to introduce the new sight vocabulary or decoding skills needed for each story, a few minutes devoted to their introduction will only make the lesson more rewarding for the children working with the texts. The symbols ℘ ℃ indicate an episodic break that allows a story to be worked with over two or more class periods

Arthur M. Pittis